T0087106

Moritz Moszkowski
1854–1925

20 Petites Études
20 Little Studies
20 kleine Etüden

pour Piano
for Piano
für Klavier

opus 91

Edité par / Edited by / Herausgegeben von
Philipp Marguerre

ED 22650
ISMN 979-0-001-16348-4

www.schott-music.com

Mainz · London · Berlin · Madrid · New York · Paris · Prague · Tokyo · Toronto
© 2019 SCHOTT MUSIC GmbH & Co. KG, Mainz · Printed in Germany

Vorwort

Moritz (Maurycy) Moszkowski wurde am 23. August 1854 in Breslau geboren. Dort erhielt er den ersten Musikunterricht. In Berlin studierte er am 1850 gegründeten Stern'schen Konservatorium sowie am Kullakschen Konservatorium, wo ihn u.a. Theodor Kullak (der heutzutage noch für seine Unterrichtswerke bekannt ist) unterrichtete. Er war mit den Brüdern Scharwenka sowie mit Franz Liszt näher bekannt.

In der zweiten Hälfte des 19. Jahrhunderts wurde Moszkowski als einer der bekanntesten Vertreter der „Salonmusik" sowie als Komponist von Unterrichtswerken geschätzt. Dies belegt u.a. eine von Rodolphe (Rudolf) Strobl (1831–1915), „Professeur des classes supérieures de Piano du Conservatoire à Varsovie (Warschau)" herausgegebene Einteilung Moszkowskischer Etüden in unterschiedliche Schwierigkeitsgrade. Zum Beispiel werden einige Etüden aus op. 72 als „V. Degré" klassifiziert und direkt neben die Werke Clementis, Haydns, Mozarts, Beethovens und Schuberts gestellt.[1] Ignaz Paderewski sah Moszkowski nach Chopin als denjenigen Komponisten an, der am besten für das Klavier zu komponieren wisse. 1897 verließ Moszkowski Berlin und zog nach, wo er bis zu seinem Tode im Jahre 1925 lebte und unterrichtete. Er komponierte Opern, Kammermusik und zahlreiche Instrumentalwerke, darunter mehr als 100 Werke für Klavier.

Trotz des großen Erfolges im 19. Jahrhundert geriet Moszkowski in der Folgezeit nahezu in Vergessenheit. Einige wenige Werke, wie die *Étincelles* op. 36 Nr. 6 aus den *Acht charakteristischen Stücken*, die Vladimir Horowitz mitunter in seinen Solo-Rezitals vortrug, die *Serenade* op. 15 oder das zusammen mit seinem Bruder Alexander verfasste satirische Variationswerk *Anton Notenquetscher am Clavier* sind heute noch im Repertoire des Pianisten zu finden.

Die *20 Petites Études* (Erstveröffentlichung 1913) sind im leicht bis mittelschweren Bereich einzuordnen. Die Aufgabenstellungen sind unterschiedlich, vom Triolen- und Unisonospiel bis zur Zweistimmigkeit in einer Hand, doch spürbar vor allem auf die Geläufigkeit des angehenden Pianisten ausgelegt. Die spieltechnischen Aufgabenstellungen werden im Register aufgelistet. Alle Etüden zeichnen sich durch einen guten Klaviersatz und eine überschaubare Länge aus, was für ein konzentriertes Üben sehr förderlich ist.

Nahezu alle Etüden haben den Charakter ausgelassener Capricen, und nur vereinzelt zeichnen sich einige Etüden durch eine gewisse „humorvolle Strenge" und liedhaften Charakter aus, etwa die Etüden Nr. 10, 13 und 20, von welchen lediglich zwei in einer Molltonart stehen. Die letzten vier Etüden sind vom Charakter her kantabler, doch nicht minder pianistisch, und führen zur abschließenden Etüde hin, die in ges-Moll steht. Diese endet, ebenso wie die drei vorigen, nicht mit einem fulminanten Abschluss, sondern ruhig und versonnen.

Die Fingersätze sind der 1931 von Isidor Philipp bei Alphonse Leduc herausgegebenen Ausgabe entnommen.

Philipp Alexander Marguerre

---

[1] Rodolphe Strobl, „Choix de Compositions classiques et modernes. Les œuvres ci-dessus sont recommandées à jouer en même temps que les œuvres de Clementi, Haydn, Mozart, Beethoven, Schubert et d'autres."

Klaviertechnische Aufgabenstellungen der einzelnen Etüden

Aufgabenstellung	Etüde Nr.
Alternieren der Hände	15
Akkordspiel	13
Akkordbrechungen	11, 12, 15, 17
Chromatik	20
„Daumen"-Melodie vgl. Chopin op. 25 Nr. 1	15
Doppelgriffe in Terzen, Sexten und anderen Kombinationen	9, 13, 14, 20
Geläufigkeit	1-7, 11, 12, 14, 15, 16, 18, 19
Kantables Spiel	8, 10, 13, 17, 20
Lagenwechsel	4, 9, 13, 18
Melodie in der linken Hand	13, 17
Oktaven	17
Pedal	17
Repetitionen	4, 12
Triolen / Sextolen etc.	16, 18, 19
Unisonospiel	16
Zweistimmigkeit in einer Hand	4, 8, 10

Preface

Moritz (Maurycy) Moszkowski was born on 23 August 1854 in Breslau (Wrocław), where he began his musical education. He went on to study in Berlin at the Stern Conservatory, founded in 1850, and at the Kullak Academy, where his teachers included Theodor Kullak, still known today for his tutorial works. Moszkowski became acquainted with the Scharwenka brothers and with Franz Liszt.

In the second half of the nineteenth Century Moszkowski became well known for his 'salon music' and as a composer of tutorial pieces. Documentary evidence of his popularity includes an edition of Moszkowki's studies graded according to difficulty by Rodolphe (Rudolf) Strobl (1831-1915), '*professeur des classes supérieures de Piano du Conservatoire à Varsovie (Warsaw)*'. Studies No. 7, 9, 11 and 14, for example, were classified as '*V. degré*' and placed alongside works by Clementi, Haydn, Mozart, Beethoven and Schubert.[1] Ignaz Paderewski considered Moszkowski second only to Chopin in knowing how to write for the piano. Moszkowski left Berlin in 1897 and moved to Paris, where he lived and taught piano until his death in 1925. He composed operas, chamber music and numerous instrumental pieces, including more than a hundred pieces for the piano.

Despite his great success in the nineteenth Century, Moszkowski was subsequently almost forgotten. A few of his pieces still feature today in the repertoire for pianists, such as *Étincelles* Op. 36 No. 6 from *Eight Characteristic Pieces*, which Vladimir Horovitz included in his solo recitals, the *Serenade* Op. 15 or the satirical set of variations *Anton Note-Crusher at the Piano*, which Moszkowski wrote with his brother Alexander.

These *20 Petites Études* (first published in 1913) are at easy to intermediate standard. They focus on various challenges, from playing triplets and playing in unison to combining two parts with one hand, though the primary emphasis for the aspiring pianist is on developing fluent playing at speed. The techniques covered are identified in the index. All these *Études* are characterised by good piano writing and manageable length – highly desirable for useful practice.

Almost all the *Études* are in the manner of playful caprices, while a few individual *Études* have a certain 'humorous rigour' and lyrical character, such as *Études* Nos. 10, 13 and 20: only two of these are in a minor key. The last four *Études* are more *cantabile*, but no less pianistic in style, leading through to the final *Étude* in G♭ minor. Like the three preceding *Études*, this does not end with a thundering climax, but in calm and reflective mood.

Fingerings given are those used by Isidor Philipp in the 1931 edition published by Alphonse Leduc.

Philipp Alexander Marguerre
Translation Julia Rushworth

---

[1] Rodolphe Strobl, 'Choix de Compositions classiques et modernes. Les œuvres ci-dessus sont recommandées à jouer en même temps que les œuvres de Clementi, Haydn, Mozart, Beethoven, Schubert et d'autres.'

Technical challenges dealt with in individual etudes

Technique	Étude No.
Alternating hands	15
Playing chords	13
Broken chords	11, 12, 15, 17
Chromaticism	20
Playing melodic line with the thumbs, cf. Chopin op. 25 No. 1	15
Parallel thirds, sixths and other combinations	9, 13, 14, 20
Playing fluently at speed	1-7, 11, 12, 14, 15, 16, 18, 19
Cantabile tone	8, 10, 13, 17, 20
Position changes	4, 9, 13, 18
Melody in the left hand	13, 17
Octaves	17
Using the pedal	17
Repeated notes	4, 12
Triplets, sextuplets etc.	16, 18, 19
Playing in unison	16
Playing two parts with one hand	4, 8, 10

Préface

Moritz (Maurycy) Moszkowski naît le 23 août 1854 à Breslau (Vratislavie) où il reçoit sa première formation musicale. Il poursuit ses études à Berlin au Conservatoire Stern'sches, fondé en 1850, et à la Kullaksche Akademie, où il a notamment pour professeur Theodor Kullak, connu encore aujourd'hui pour ses méthodes d'apprentissage. Il compte parmi ses connaissances les compositeurs Philipp et Xaver Scharwenka, ainsi que Franz Liszt.

Moszkowski devient l'un des représentants les plus connus de la musique de salon et se fait un nom comme auteur de manuels d'apprentissage. C'est ce que montre notamment l'édition de ses études par Rodolphe Strobl (1831–1915), « Professeur des classes supérieures de piano du Conservatoire à Varsovie », où elles sont classées par degré de difficulté. Les études n°s 7, 9, 11 et 14 appartiennent par exemple au « Ve Degré » et figurent à côté d'œuvres de Clementi, Haydn, Mozart, Beethoven et Schubert[1]. Pour Ignace Paderewski, Moszkowski est le plus grand compositeur de musique pour piano après Chopin. En 1897, Moszkowski quitte Berlin et va s'installer à Paris où il vivra et enseignera jusqu'à sa mort, en 1925. Il compose des opéras, de la musique de chambre et de nombreuses pages instrumentales, notamment plus de cent œuvres pour piano.

Après avoir connu un grand succès au XIXe siècle, Moszkowski tombe presque complètement dans l'oubli. Quelques rares pages de sa plume – les *Étincelles* op. 36 n° 6 tiré du recueil *Huit Pièces caractéristiques*, que Vladimir Horowitz jouait parfois en récital, la *Sérénade* op. 15, ou *Anton Notenquetscher am Clavier*, œuvre satirique qu'il écrivit avec son frère Alexander – figurent encore aujourd'hui au répertoire des pianistes.

Les *20 Petites Études*, dont la première édition remonte à 1913, sont d'un niveau facile à moyennement difficile. Les difficultés techniques qu'elles font travailler sont diverses, depuis les triolets jusqu'à une polyphonie à deux voix dans une seule main en passant par le jeu à l'unisson, mais destinées à développer la vélocité de l'apprenti pianiste. Ces aspects techniques sont répertoriés dans un index. Toutes les études sont parfaitement écrites pour le piano et relativement courtes, ce qui est idéal pour travailler de manière concentrée.

Presque toutes ont le caractère de caprices enjoués, quelques-unes seulement se distinguent par une « rigueur humoristique » et un certain lyrisme, par exemple les N° 10, 13 et 20, dont seules deux sont en mineur. Les quatre dernières études sont plutôt chantantes mais pas moins pianistiques pour autant. La toute dernière, en *sol* bémol mineur, s'achève comme les trois précédentes, non pas en fanfare, mais de manière calme et réfléchie.

Les doigtés sont empruntés à l'édition Alphonse Leduc de 1931 et dus à Isidor Philipp.

Philipp Alexander Marguerre
Traduction Daniel Fesquet

---

[1] Rodolphe Strobl, « Choix de Compositions classiques et modernes. Les œuvres ci-dessus sont recommandées à jouer en même temps que les œuvres de Clementi, Haydn, Mozart, Beethoven, Schubert et d'autres. »

Index des difficultés techniques des études

Aspect technique	Étude n°
Mains alternées	15
Accords	13
Accords brisés	11, 12, 15, 17
Chromatismes	20
Mélodie du pouce (cf. Étude op. 25 n° 1 de Chopin)	15
Traits en tierces, en sixtes et autres	9, 13, 14, 20
Vélocité	1-7, 11, 12, 14, 15, 16, 18, 19
Cantabile	8, 10, 13, 17, 20
Déplacements	4, 9, 13, 18
Mélodie à la main gauche	13, 17
Octaves	17
Pédale	17
Notes répétées	4, 12
Triolets, sextolets etc.	16, 18, 19
Unisson	16
Polyphonie à deux voix dans une main	4, 8, 10

Inhalt / Contents / Contenu

À Madame M. T. Amirian

20 Petites Études
opus 91

No. 1

Moritz Moszkowski
1854–1925

Con moto (♩ = 132)

12

No. 2

No. 3

Vivace ($\quarternote$ = 152)

No. 4

No. 5

No. 6

Allegro ma non troppo (♩. = 152)

No. 7

No. 8

Moderato (♩ = 96)

il basso sempre legato

No. 9

No. 10

No. 11

Allegro ma non troppo (♩ = 126)

No. 12

36

No. 13

Con moto ma non troppo (♩ = 112)

No. 14

No. 15

Allegro non troppo ma molto energico ($\text{♩} = 132$)

44

No. 16

Allegro energico ($\text{♩.} = 168$)

No. 17

No. 18

Vivo (♩ = 126)

No. 19

No. 20

Allegro moderato ($\downarrow = 60$)